When DOING GOOD THINGS
is not GOOD ENOUGH

When DOING GOOD THINGS is not GOOD ENOUGH

The Story of CORNELIUS THE CENTURION

Robert "Bob" Lewis

XULON ELITE

Xulon Press Elite
555 Winderley Pl, Suite 225
Maitland, FL 32751
407.339.4217
www.xulonpress.com

© 2024 by Robert "Bob" Lewis

All rights reserved solely by the author. The author guarantees all contents are original and do not infringe upon the legal rights of any other person or work. No part of this book may be reproduced in any form without the permission of the author.

Due to the changing nature of the Internet, if there are any web addresses, links, or URLs included in this manuscript, these may have been altered and may no longer be accessible. The views and opinions shared in this book belong solely to the author and do not necessarily reflect those of the publisher. The publisher therefore disclaims responsibility for the views or opinions expressed within the work.

Unless otherwise indicated, Scripture quotations taken from the New King James Version (NKJV). Copyright © 1982 by Thomas Nelson, Inc. Used by permission. All rights reserved.

Paperback ISBN-13: 979-8-86850-054-1
Ebook ISBN-13: 979-8-86850-055-8

Table of Contents

Preface vii

Introduction ix

Chapter 1: **Introducing Luke** 1

Chapter 2: **Introducing Cornelius** 7

Chapter 3: **Cornelius's Account** 13

Chapter 4: **Luke Continues** 21

Chapter 5: **Introducing Peter** 29

Chapter 6: **Peter Continues** 37

Chapter 7: **Peter Meets Cornelius** 45

Chapter 8: **Peter Continues** 57

Chapter 9: **The Holy Spirit Falls on the Gentiles** 65

Chapter 10: **Paul Meets With the Jerusalem Council** 75

Chapter 11: **More Conversation Between Luke and Peter** . . . 85

Preface

This story of Cornelius has always been of great interest to me. Here was a man who was introduced to us, the readers, in Acts 10:1–6 as *"a devout man…. who feared God with all his household, who gave alms to the people, and prayed to God always."* The story continues when an angel of God appears to him, telling him his *"prayers and alms have come up for a memorial before God"* and that he should send for Simon Peter who will tell him what he must do.

And the story further continues with how God—through the working of the Holy Spirit—was able to bring so many factors together at the same time so that 1) Peter was ready and willing to share the gospel message with someone who was not a Jew and 2) Cornelius was ready and willing to receive an important message from Simon Peter, who he had never met. All he knew about Simon Peter was that he was probably just a Jewish man and no one of great importance.

Obviously, the two main characters in this story are Simon Peter the disciple/apostle and Cornelius the centurion. Their story was compiled by the author of the Book of Acts who most students of the Bible agree was Luke, the physician. That being true,

I believe it would be beneficial to include him in this story because he meets with each of them to hear and record their individual accounts of their story.

Often, I read the Bible and miss much of what is being said because I don't take time to look closely at all that is recorded. That is why each time we read the Bible something different may get our attention and we wonder: *How did I not see that the other times I have read this passage?* Perhaps you have felt the same?

My hope and prayer is that this book will inspire you to look a little closer at the scriptures as you read them. Maybe it will cause you to dream about what it might have been like to have known Cornelius (who was a well-respected centurion). Or to have known Peter who was a guy who often said things that he wished he hadn't said, whose life was forever changed after the day of Pentecost.

Maybe Luke the physician will inspire you to think beyond the limits you have placed upon yourself. Though he had a medical practice that would have kept him busy, he felt it was important to record as much information as he could about the life and ministry of Jesus. If that was not enough, he also felt it would be advantageous to record as many stories as he could about the work of the Holy Spirit since the day of Pentecost.

But the real question I believe we need to keep before us in this story is this: *what was it that Simon Peter was supposed to tell Cornelius that he needed to do, and why?*

Introduction

What was Peter doing in Joppa?

Peter had been traveling as an evangelist missionary to wherever he was given opportunity to preach the gospel. His preaching had been very successful—so much so that Simon, the tanner of Joppa, had opened his home to him (see Acts 9:43).

Perhaps Simon Peter went there soon after the death of Stephen (see Acts 7:54–60), when many of the early believers were led to leave Jerusalem because of the persecution that had become more prevalent. On the other hand, one of the last things Jesus told them was, *"Go into all the world and preach the gospel!"* (see Mark 16:15).

It would seem that God was using this newfound relationship with Simon the tanner to break down some walls that Peter had in his life. This new convert's occupation would not fit well into the stereotype that Peter had grown up with; handling of dead bodies (even that of animals) as much as he did would certainly be hard to justify in the Law.

Who was this man known as Cornelius?

Cornelius was a centurion who was stationed at Caesarea as commander of the Italian Regiment which consisted of 100 soldiers. He was a very religious man who prayed very often and was very generous toward other people. Not much is known about him before the events of Acts 10 and he is never mentioned again after Acts 11. But his story is very important for all believers—both Jewish and non-Jewish.

Why is understanding the author (Luke) important to this story?

Luke wrote not only the Book of Acts, but also the Gospel of Luke. In Luke 1:1–4 he explains his reason for writing the Gospel of Luke, which I am sure also had some bearing as to why he wrote the Book of Acts. In that gospel, his goal was to set in some semblance of order the teachings and ministry of Jesus—both what He accomplished and what was fulfilled by Him.

In Acts, Luke's goal was not to follow Peter, or Paul, or even the other disciples. His goal was tracking (and recording) the movement of the Holy Spirit—how the Spirit was moving in the lives and ministry of those who were being used in many different ways. Luke also wrote about how lives were changed when new believers' lives were touched by the Holy Spirit.

So, I think it best to start by introducing Luke the physician before getting to the story of the encounter between Peter the apostle and Cornelius the centurion.

CHAPTER 1
Introducing Luke

I have always been amazed at how God leads us throughout our lives. Even as a young boy, I always wanted to be a doctor. I dreamed of the day when I could hang up a sign on my door that said simply: the OFFICE OF DR. LUKE! I dreamed of the day when the sick could come to my office for help and I would understand their condition and be able to help them!

And everything seemed to be going according to plan until the day I heard about this man from Nazareth who was going around the countryside preaching and teaching, and even performing miracles of healing. I say the countryside, but he was also doing these things in Jerusalem, even at the temple.

So, like everyone else, I wanted to see for myself what was happening. Some were even saying that maybe He was to be the Deliverer! The One who would lead all of Israel out of bondage! Of course, I had my doubts. I knew the Scriptures and prophecies about the Coming One. He would be born in Bethlehem, but everyone was already saying He was from Nazareth. And like the old saying goes, "Can anything good come out of Nazareth?"

Being a doctor—though I was just getting started at the time—I knew enough to know that He was not using any kind of magic tricks or deception. Much of what He was doing would have to be classified as miraculous, as the things being reported were out of the realm of medicine. As a doctor, I have to admit that it was puzzling to me that He never used any kind of medicine that I as a doctor was taught to use. In fact, as far as I know He never used any type of medicine at all! Some of the people He healed, He did so just by touching them. Others were healed by just His words, and some were healed—even raised from the dead—when He wasn't even with them. All He ever did was touch or speak to people, and they were healed!

But one thing that really got my attention was the occasion where He told the sick person that his sins were forgiven, which also got the attention of the Pharisees and other religious leaders (see Mark 2:3–12). His response to their questions was this: "Is it easier to say, 'Your sins are forgiven' or 'take up your bed and walk?'" And then He spoke those words to the man, "Take up your bed and walk," and he walked; he was healed.

> **If He was to be the Deliverer, maybe His way of delivering us was not going to be quite what we expected.**

Of course, I never got the opportunity to actually talk to Jesus or even meet Him. But all the stories I heard about Him certainly paved the way for me to want to know more about Him.

These events, His many other miracles, His teaching, His boldness, and even His humility all led me to follow His ministry closely. If He was to be the Deliverer, maybe His way of delivering us was not going to be quite what we expected. And sure enough, when He died on the cross as a criminal (though He was innocent) we all thought He had lost the battle. But three days later He rose from the dead! Now, we who believed in Him know that His way of delivering us is much different than we ever expected—which pretty much follows right along with how His answer to our prayers is often much different than we would have expected.

And that leads me to the story of a Roman centurion named Cornelius (see Acts 10) that the Apostle Peter met with at the city of Caesarea, whose story I had learned of from the leaders of the church in Jerusalem (see Acts 11:1–18). Peter had shared with the church leaders how he had been able to preach the gospel to this Roman centurion, and the man had actually become a "believer." I had questions for Peter about the whole encounter that I wanted to ask him that had to do with why he went to meet with him, what his message to him was, and how he knew he had become a believer.

The early Church was being led mainly by the twelve disciples, but also by others who were learned scholars who had become believers after witnessing the death and resurrection of Jesus. Several of these new leaders were actually Pharisees and Sadducees. It seemed that many of them could not be convinced to remain in the old established ways, though most of them still wanted to hold on to some of their traditions (more on that later). Evidently, God was doing something new, and they were hoping to be part of it.

I must admit the thought had crossed my mind that these leaders could actually have been sent to kind of spy out this new movement of Jesus's followers to prevent them from becoming too large or powerful. Their movement was already causing a lot of problems at the temple for the religious leaders. Also, I couldn't help but wonder how the "chemistry" would be between the disciples who actually followed Jesus for three years and the Pharisees, Sadducees, and other religious leaders who had grown up studying under the very leaders who were still leading the Jewish religion.

I thought it would be good to hear the story from both Cornelius and Peter the apostle. It was obvious when I finally got to meet with each of them that the Holy Spirit was really at work in both of them at the same time. I think it is intriguing in some ways how the Holy Spirit leads us one step at a time. He often shows us just a small piece of what we are to do, and when we have that done, He shows a little bit more. I know that has been true in my own life, and I believe that was also the case here—especially with Peter. God was going to have to break down a lot of walls in Peter's thinking if He was going to use him to reach people with the gospel.

Though I actually met with Simon Peter first, I think it would be best to start with Cornelius's account in this story. When I met Cornelius, several years had passed since he had that meeting with Peter.

Discussion Questions

1. Knowing that Jesus was from Nazareth made it hard for people to believe that He could be their Deliverer, especially if they knew the prophecies from Scripture. Where was he supposed to be born (according to prophecy)? Why did God find it necessary to keep the truth of his birthplace hidden?

_____

_____

_____

_____

2. Why were the leaders of the church in Jerusalem (Acts 11) so concerned about Peter going to the home of Cornelius? Why were they willing to accept his explanation so quickly?

_____

_____

_____

_____

3. Was "legalism" a problem for the early church, and why? Which leaders would have wanted to continue being legalistic, and which ones would have rejected it? How can we avoid legalism today?

_____

_____

_____

_____

CHAPTER 2

Introducing Cornelius

> *There was a certain man in Caesarea called Cornelius, a centurion of what was called the Italian Regiment, a devout man and one who feared God with all his household, who gave alms generously to the people, and prayed to God always.* (Acts 10:1–2)

Ever since he had been relocated from Jerusalem to Caesarea, Cornelius' attitude toward the Jewish people had changed. He had always thought of them as being a very peculiar clan of people—an odd mix of humility and arrogance—with all their talk about "the One True God," and being "God's chosen people." If they were really the One True God's chosen people, why were they always forced to live in such humble ways. Their beliefs and way of life always seemed to be rather foolish.

He had grown up his entire life believing there were different gods to pray to for different needs.

What made them think they were any different from any other people or country? He had grown up his entire life believing there were different gods to pray to for different needs. It made perfect sense to him that there would be many gods to pray to; there was just no way that one, two, three, or even just ten gods could help all of mankind with all the different needs that everyone faced every day. There were gods to pray to for rain, for harvest, for fertility, for sickness, for health, for finances, for new chariots, for _____. You name it, there was a god to pray to for it!

But the Jews! They believed that there was only one true God—JEHOVAH—who governed over all the affairs of man; and that someday everyone (all of mankind) would bow before Him and worship Him.

And for some reason they were His chosen people. They believed that this God would someday send a deliverer—and the world (at least their world) would change forever. But their history over the past thousand plus years was not very impressive. If this God they claimed to serve really existed, He sure had a strange way of taking care of them.

Or, maybe Cornelius's change of attitude about them wasn't so much about being relocated to Caesarea; maybe it had more to do with the timing of his relocation. There was that man there at the time that everyone thought was a prophet—maybe even their soon-coming king! Jesus was his name.

Cornelius had never in his life witnessed anything like what he saw happening during his time there. So many of those Jewish people had been following Him; kind of hanging on His every word. And some of the stories they told about healings, miracles, even His teachings were almost beyond belief!

And then to hear about those people turning on Him and treating him like a criminal. And the people who were responsible for most of the hate toward him were actually the Jewish leaders—their so-called "spiritual" leaders nonetheless!

++++++++++++++++++++++++++

Luke's Observation

Before going to meet with Cornelius, I thought it would be beneficial to learn as much as I could about him. I learned that he was known to be a man "who gave alms generously to the people, and prayed to God always" (Acts 10:2b). It did not matter who they were—they might be Roman, they might be citizens of Caesarea, or of Jerusalem when he served there. They might even be natives of Africa. They might be travelers just passing through his city who needed help—it didn't matter; if he saw someone in need, he found a way to help them. He even helped the Israelites when he saw they were in need!

He was not your typical Roman soldier; he had always been a very caring leader, which is why so many of his household servants and the soldiers under his command had such great respect for him. Not one of the soldiers under his command was looking to be transferred; that says a lot about him as a leader and as a person.

Although soldiers who are happy where they are at are often the ones chosen for transfers.

Obviously, these things were true about Cornelius even before his meeting with Peter the Apostle. He was highly respected at Caesarea, and he was also highly respected when he served at Jerusalem. Even the Jewish people thought highly of him.

These things that I've mentioned so far about him I did not learn from him. When I met him, I could tell right away that he was a humble man, one who did not like to talk about himself. What I've mentioned so far, I learned from my previous meeting with Simon Peter and also from talking with his servants, the soldiers under his command, and even a few Jews who remembered him from when he served at Jerusalem. He was a man who was greatly loved and respected! He did not seem to demand respect, but he certainly did command respect. It was easy to show respect to him, soldier or not.

His servants also told me that he was a man who prayed a lot. I found this to be very interesting considering that he was a Roman soldier, given the fact that Romans always looked down on the Jewish people and often made light of the Jewish religion. So, I thought perhaps that prayer would be a good place to start when I met with him. Was there something specific he was praying about, and to what god was he praying?

DISCUSSION QUESTIONS

1. Knowing what we know about Cornelius in the first two verses of Acts 10, what would most people say about him and his relationship with God?

_____

_____

_____

_____

2. Do you know someone who believes that if they live a "good enough" life then God will accept them into heaven when they die? How could you use Cornelius's story to help them see the truth about faith instead of works?

_____

_____

_____

_____

3. Though we normally think of gods as something (or someone) we pray to, are there things that we value today that might take the place of God?

CHAPTER 3

Cornelius's Account

ACTS 10:3-8

One day a man came to visit me saying he wanted to talk with me about the time (several years ago now) that I had a life-changing meeting with the Jewish apostle called Simon Peter. His name was Luke, and he was a physician. He said he had learned about me from Simon Peter and other leaders of the group that was becoming known as The Way (see Acts 9:2), and he wanted to hear of my involvement in the story. He was interested in my story because he wanted to put together some type of book or documentary that would detail accounts of how not only Jewish people were becoming followers of Jesus, many non-Jewish people were too.

Obviously, I was quite surprised that he would want to hear my story of when I came to understand who Jesus was—and is. It must have been pretty obvious to him that I did not know where to start in telling my story, so he mentioned that some of my servants had said that I was a man who seemed to pray a lot. Had this always been true about me? Was there a specific god that I prayed to more than others? Or had something happened in my life that caused me to start praying more than in the past?

Well actually, YES, there was! I had been in Jerusalem during the days that Jesus was there, before He was killed. Though many of my fellow soldiers mocked Him, and the people who were hanging on His every word, I noticed that many people who listened to His teachings seemed to be very different after hearing Him and spending time with Him. They seemed to be more relaxed and content, less worried, and even happier than the other Jewish people who seemed to reject His teaching. If there is one thing that we soldiers appreciated it was when the people we oversaw didn't cause us a lot of problems. It was odd though that the people this Jesus seemed to have the most difficulty dealing with were the Jewish leaders. We soldiers laughed about it, figuring that the leaders of the people felt threatened by Him.

It was just a few weeks before His death (or murder as some prefer to describe it) that I was transferred to Caesarea to be the commander of this contingent of soldiers, so I never saw everything that transpired—but I sure heard about it. A number of the soldiers who were there for the crucifixion have said their lives were forever changed. Perhaps He was the Coming One, the King of the Jews—but why did He have to die? What did that mean for the Jews? And what could it mean for me, since I am not a Jew?

> **A number of the soldiers who were there for the crucifixion have said their lives were forever changed.**

But, what was it that had caused me to start praying more? I actually was not aware that I was praying more than normal. Evidently my servants and others close to me, noticed the difference in me. So, it is hard to explain something that I was not aware was happening. It may have had something to do with the fact that the Jewish people, especially the religious leaders, had wanted to crucify this man that so many had believed would be their deliverer.

Many were saying that this Jesus had actually risen from the dead and that a large number of people had seen Him after He died on more than one occasion, but that all seemed so farfetched. Anyone can claim that they saw someone who was raised from the dead, but no one could prove it by showing Him to the governing authorities when ordered to do so. But, on the other hand, the authorities could not show his dead body to prove He was dead either.

Some said His followers stole His body, but I knew some of the soldiers who were on duty during the time He was supposed to be dead and inside the tomb. It seems impossible that Jesus's followers would have been able to overpower those soldiers. They would have to roll away the stone that had been placed in front of the tomb, and take out His beaten, mangled body that had been wrapped in grave clothes for more than 36 hours minimum. If He wasn't dead when He was placed in the tomb, then the grave clothes would have suffocated Him. All the authorities would have to do was produce the body of the man they had crucified and that would have stopped all of the stories of Him rising from the dead.

But, here we are now, several years after the death of Jesus, and His followers are still proclaiming that He rose from the dead, and somehow they are gaining followers. And then it kind of dawned on me—I was finding myself praying to this God of the Jews more than I was praying to the gods that I had grown up with all my life. Yet, even then I felt like something was missing.

I thought that maybe if I treated people fairly and helped those who were poor and needy that it would make a difference. It did make a difference in how I felt about myself, but I also knew something was still missing. I also realized that somehow during this time I had replaced all the gods that I had prayed to all my life and instead was only praying to this God that the Jewish people called Jehovah.

I had been doing this for I don't really know how long—maybe several months. Then one day, at *about the ninth hour of the day I saw clearly in a vision an angel of God coming in and saying to me, "Cornelius!" And when I observed him, I was afraid, and said, "What is it, Lord?" So he said to me, "your prayers and your alms have come up for a memorial before God. Now send men to Joppa, and send for Simon whose surname is Peter. He is lodging with Simon, a tanner, whose house is by the sea. He will tell you what you must do." And when the angel who spoke to me had departed, I called two of my household servants and a devout soldier from among those who waited on me continually. So when I had explained all these things to them, I sent them to Joppa.*

I thought it was kind of odd when this man named Luke asked if he could quote me on what I had just told him; I said I suppose so.

That is how I remember everything that happened in my dream—or vision—about the angel of God.

So, what did I do? I did exactly what the angel told me to do. I sent two of my household servants and my most reliable soldier to Joppa to get this man Simon Peter to come meet with me. I'm sure my orders probably seemed odd to all three of them, but I told them it was very important that they make haste in returning.

So, for the next few days I waited, not knowing what to do or what to expect. I expected the journey would take all of four days. I didn't know if I should be worried, or scared, or excited; I was at a loss as to what to do or feel. So I started pondering what the angel had said to me: *"Your prayers and alms have come up for a memorial before God"* (Acts 10:4b).

Well, surely that had to be a good thing, right? The angel of God didn't sound upset with me. So, I felt that whatever was going to happen would be a good thing. This guy named Peter was going to answer some questions for me; the only problem I could see was that I didn't know what questions to ask. And then the light came on for me: this man named Peter was going to tell me *what I must do!* In trying to learn how to serve this newfound God of the Jews that I was praying to, I just felt like there was always something I needed to do, but I was never sure what that "something" was.

My confidence was beginning to grow in this God called Jehovah. Whatever it was this man named Peter was going to tell me that was so important, I felt like it would be worthwhile for all my family to hear it, and even my servants. Maybe even some of the soldiers under my command could benefit from it too. So, I invited everyone I could think of that might be interested in what this man had to say to be at my home when he arrived.

Discussion Questions

1. Two reasons are given as to why it was unlikely that Jesus's body was stolen; what are some other reasons it would be unlikely that His body was taken or stolen or that He really wasn't dead?

_____

_____

_____

_____

2. In Acts 10:4b Cornelius is told, "Your prayers and your alms have come up for a memorial before God." What is significant about this statement by the angel?

_____

_____

_____

_____

3. Since we know that "faith without works is dead" and that our "good works" will not save us, why is Cornelius told that Peter "will tell you what you must do"?

_____

_____

_____

_____

CHAPTER 4

Luke Continues

I have always enjoyed writing, doing research, and learning new things, especially things that have to do with the ongoing stories about Jesus's ministry through his disciples (even though leading officials still say He is dead). My original thought was that this would be an exciting and maybe even an important project to work on that could be helpful for other people. But, I also must admit that my curiosity probably had a lot to do with me wanting to know as much as I could about everything that had happened since Jesus was crucified.

I sincerely wanted to learn all the stories I could about how the Holy Spirit was actively working in and through the disciples of Jesus since He had died on that cross. I am thankful for the time I was able to put into recording all I have learned about all that Jesus accomplished while He was here as a man. All of the prophecies He fulfilled throughout His life—from His birth to His death and His Resurrection; I have been encouraged by others to write out all I have learned about Him. Perhaps it can be of benefit to others in the future.

I am reminded of the story of Moses when he met God at the burning bush (see Exodus 4:1–5). God was calling him to lead Israel out of slavery in Egypt. Moses could not quite comprehend that God wanted to use him to lead the people, so he kept offering reasons (or excuses) that God could not use him. He did not believe he had much to offer as a leader, so God told him to take his staff and throw it to the ground. As a shepherd of sheep, it was one of his most important tools he possessed to lead, guide, and protect his sheep. God revealed to Moses that God would use him and his staff to show the Israelites and Pharaoh His power. God can make use of anything we possess to accomplish His will if we will give it to Him. I believe this is true of my desire to write and do research also!

> **God can make use of anything we possess to accomplish His will if we will give it to Him.**

There have been so many amazing stories I have been told about people that the Holy Spirit is working in and through. I am sure I will be hearing and experiencing even more as time goes on. The Holy Spirit will continue to do some amazing things in and through those disciples as they continue to step out in faith. The Holy Spirit is now residing in all true believers. In fact, I will be bold enough

> **I really believe God wants us to step out in faith and do the impossible— things that we can't do without God's help; things that He has chosen to do with our help.**

to say that any believer who feels led to step out in faith and to do what they believe God is compelling them to do will see great things accomplished. I really believe God wants us to step out in faith and do the impossible—things that we can't do without God's help; things that He has chosen to do with our help. Even now, I am aware that most of the disciples are planning to start traveling to distant lands to take the good news of Jesus's Resurrection to other people that have not heard of Him yet.

I believe that just as Jesus led his disciples by example, those very disciples are now realizing that they too need to lead by example—not just by word. Our faith in Christ will continue to grow and mature as we lead new followers by our example. Perhaps other new believers will do the same.

I have always believed in the omnipotent (all-powerful) God, who is also the omniscient (all-knowing) God, but what happened next in Peter's part of the story still amazes me. It was while Cornelius's servants and a soldier were traveling to Joppa to get Peter that Peter went up on the rooftop to pray. That was not surprising—it is common practice to go off alone to pray during the day. The roof of your home is a great place to spend your time in prayer.

What amazed me though was when Peter became hungry while praying he had a vision of a large sheet coming down to the earth from the heavens. It was filled with all kinds of wild beasts, bugs, and birds—and not the kind a good Jewish man would expect. Everything that was in the vision was considered unclean by all Jewish people; they were not to be eaten according to the

Law handed down by Moses. This happened to Peter three times, and each time Peter said: "*No! I have never eaten anything common or unclean!*" And each time a voice spoke to him: "*What God has cleansed you must not call common* (Acts 10:14–15)!"

It was also quite interesting who Simon Peter was staying with at the time. He was staying in the home of a man named Simon, who was a tanner (see Acts 9:43). He was a recent convert and had made his home available to Simon Peter to stay in while he was at Joppa. This was something that Jesus had told the disciples they should do when they traveled to other cities sharing the gospel message. And He also told them what to do if their message was not received—they should shake the dust from their feet as they left that town (see Matthew 10:14).

But, getting back to the new convert that Simon Peter was staying with—Simon the tanner. People in that profession were looked down on by religious leaders because they were in contact with dead animals so often. It was considered wrong to associate with someone of that class. They were considered unclean; in fact, according to the law, a tanner had to live at least seventy-five feet outside a village because of his constant ritual uncleanness. It was such a vile and contemptuous type of work that if a girl was betrothed to a tanner without knowing it then the betrothal contract could be voided. Their occupation was that bad![1]

Peter had just realized recently that even a tanner could become a believer—within weeks of having the vision of the large sheet filled with unclean animals, and being told not to call

---

[1] (enduringword.com/bible-commentary/acts-9/ 2018 Author David Guzik)

anything unclean that God has said is now clean! Apparently, God was up to something—something new and unheard of—as Peter was making his way around the nation preaching and teaching the good news of Jesus to anyone that would listen.

As much as I like to tell all these stories myself that have arisen about the activities of the disciples since the Resurrection of Jesus the Christ, I think for now it would be best if I let Peter and Cornelius tell their stories of their involvement in what the Holy Spirit is and was doing, especially in this account involving Cornelius.

Discussion Questions

1. Luke makes the statement: "I really believe God wants us to step out in faith and do the impossible—things that we can't do without His help; things that He has chosen to do with our help." What does this statement mean to you? Have there been times in your life when you have tried to step out in faith? And what was the outcome?

2. Name five people in your life who were/are examples of faithful living. What was it that impressed you most about their lives?

3. Name five people who might be looking to you as an example of faithful living. What could you do that would help them better understand your walk of faith?

___

___

___

___

4. As Luke the physician found it possible to do something of value with his interest in writing and research, and Moses found that God could use his shepherd staff to lead His people, what do you have that God can use?

___

___

___

___

CHAPTER 5

Introducing Peter

The next day, as they went on their journey and drew near the city, Peter went up on the housetop to pray, about the sixth hour. Then he became very hungry and wanted to eat; but while they made ready, he fell into a trance and saw heaven opened and an object like a great sheet bound at the four corners, descending to him and let down to the earth. In it were all kinds of four-footed animals of the earth, wild beasts, creeping things, and birds of the air.

And a voice came to him, "Rise, Peter; kill and eat." But Peter said, "Not so, Lord! For I have never eaten anything common or unclean." And a voice spoke to him again the second time, "What God has cleansed you must not call common." This was done three times. And the object was taken up into heaven again (Acts 10:9–16).

Recently, Luke, the physician, contacted me to say that he has been working on a writing project. He had already been putting into writing several stories of the life and ministry, death and resurrection of Jesus the Christ. He is not sure yet why or for what purpose he is doing all of this work when he is already a very busy man with his thriving physician practice. As the old saying goes, "If you want something done, find someone who is already busy!" If they can see that it is important to do then they will get it done. Anyway, this guy Luke has always amazed me—how he can get so many things done in a day.

Now, he is working on another writing project. He wants to track all the events that have occurred since the Day of Pentecost when the Holy Spirit was first manifested in Jerusalem in that upper room (see Acts 1:13). As I remember, Jesus had appeared to us at Bethany and told us to go back to Jerusalem and wait there for the Holy Spirit to arrive. Since we were already staying in that upper room, and it was a large enough room to house so many of us comfortably, we felt like that would be the best place for us to stay—and wait.

I am not really sure that it will be possible to track all of the things that have happened, but perhaps he can find enough stories to warrant recording the stories he learns. As John likes to say: *"If all the things Jesus did were written down for us to read, I suppose that even the world itself could not contain all the books that would be written!"* (see John 21:25). I suppose that would ring true about all the activities that the Holy Spirit will be accomplishing through believers as they step out in faith to do what He leads them to do.

Luke told me he wanted to know more about the story of my meeting with Cornelius, which he had learned about from the leadership of the Church at Jerusalem. I wasn't sure why he felt it was so important, but it was one of the first examples of a Gentile becoming a believer in Jesus the Christ. When he told me he had some questions for me that might make our time together more profitable, I said that would be a big help because I was not really sure what it was that he was looking for that would be of value.

When he said what he was looking for could be summed up in three questions, I kind of cringed at the thought. He asked what was wrong, so I told him: Whenever I think of the number three it reminds me of when Jesus told me I would deny Him three times. I told Him that I would never deny Him, but He told me I would. And, of course, He was right. Then later, after He rose from the dead, He came to us when we had gone fishing and asked me three times if I loved Him. Of course I insisted that I did.

Sometimes, I look at my past and wonder what He sees in me and why He would want me. But since then He has given me opportunity to share the gospel message to individuals, to small groups, to hundreds, and even to thousands. I know it is not me that is making the difference in seeing His will accomplished. If I always did everything right then I would probably try to take the credit. But everything good that has happened in me is all because of Him!

Evidently, God was willing to forgive anyone of their sins; it did not matter their profession, their ethnicity, their depth of sin—anyone that would come to him with repentant hearts could receive forgiveness.

Luke's first question had to do with why I went to meet with Cornelius who wasn't even a Jew. Well, for one thing, when a Roman centurion says he wants to meet with you it is a good idea to do as he requests. But, I also told Luke about my vision of the large sheet coming down from heaven with a bunch of common, unclean animals in it. I was told to "kill and eat" what was there. Of course, I declined; but I was told not to call common what God has cleansed! This vision happened three times (there's that number three again).

I sense in my spirit that God is still at work in me to help me see things as He sees them, not just from my own understanding. I can look back now and see how the vision of the large sheet prepared me to share the good news with Cornelius. And I can look back now and see how sharing the good news with Simon the tanner prepared me for the vision of the large sheet. And when Jesus was willing to go and teach Samaritans, taxpayers, and so many other sinful people, He was preparing me (actually all of us) so that all of us would be willing to preach to people like Simon the tanner. We were with Jesus for three years, though I didn't think that was enough time. Evidently He believed it was enough.

> **I sense in my spirit that God is still at work in me to help me see things as He sees them, not just from my own understanding.**

His second question for me was what my message to Cornelius would be. To be honest, at the time I did not know what my message would be because I did not know yet why Cornelius had sent for me. It is hard to give an answer when you don't know the question.

All I knew for sure was that the Holy Spirit had orchestrated this meeting with Cornelius. I would know more when I needed to know more.

Discussion Questions

1. What events in your life—failures or successes—might be helpful for others if you were to share your story with them?

_____

_____

_____

_____

2. As Peter was learning that God was willing to save anyone who would call upon Him, do you have anyone in your life that seems to be unreachable? Write down three things you might do to befriend them.

_____

_____

_____

_____

3. If you could talk to Simon Peter about some of his successes and failures, what would you ask him? What do you think his answers would be?

CHAPTER 6

Peter Continues

Now while Peter wondered within himself what this vision which he had seen meant, behold, the men who had been sent from Cornelius had made inquiry for Simon's house, and stood before the gate. And they called and asked whether Simon, whose surname was Peter, was lodging there. While Peter thought about the vision, the Spirit said to him, "Behold, three men are seeking you. Arise therefore, go down and go with them, doubting nothing; for I have sent them. Then Peter went down to the men who had been sent to him from Cornelius, and said, "Yes, I am he whom you seek. For what reason have you come?"

And they said, "Cornelius the centurion, a just man, one who fears God and has a good reputation among all the nation of the Jews, was divinely instructed by a holy angel to summon you to his house, and to hear words from you." Then he invited them in and lodged them. On the next day Peter went away with them, and some brethren from Joppa accompanied him (Acts 10:17–23).

Luke was quite interested in my observations of how God had been preparing me for the opportunities He has given me to share the good news with others. I, too, am amazed at how God is giving me so many opportunities, but I am sure I am not alone in this. I believe God is at work in all of us, as we who are disciples begin to spread out as Jesus commanded us to do after His Resurrection. We may never see one another again, so we may never know how God moves in one another's lives. But, I am sure God will always be present wherever He leads each of us!

> **I believe God is at work in all of us, as we who are disciples begin to spread out as Jesus commanded us to do after His Resurrection.**

For now, Luke wants to hear the story of my encounter with Cornelius the centurion from my perspective. What he has heard about that encounter is of great interest to him, and he thinks it would be worthwhile to have it written down for future generations to read and learn from. I suppose he is right; whenever I think back to everything that happened at Caesarea in those few days, there was so much I was learning about what God was intending to do and wanting to do through all of us who followed Him. I even realized how God had sent an angel to Cornelius to have him send for me. I am still amazed at how the Lord was at work in all the details.

So many of the things Jesus did while we disciples traveled with Him for those three years—things that we did not quite understand—have begun to make sense to us. Why did He go and share His time with that Samaritan woman (see John 4:6–26) —a woman of all things and with the past that she had? Why did He so often reach out and touch so many people who weren't even Jews? He was, obvious to us now, preparing us and helping us to see that He cared for all of mankind not just we who are Jews.

Since Luke already knew about my vision and Cornelius's vision and was just verifying what he had heard, he wanted to know why I even decided to go to Cornelius's home in the first place with his servants and the one soldier. He wanted to know if I believed I was in any danger?

Did I believe I was in any danger? Well, to be honest, it didn't happen right away, but the thought did cross my mind that maybe the Jewish leaders had devised a new plan to shut us up from preaching the good news of Jesus. They had already been successful in killing Stephen (see Acts 7:54–60), and though it had not happened at the time, Herod has since then killed James (see Acts 12:1–2). And, when Herod realized how killing James had pleased the Jewish leaders, he decided to imprison me and have me killed after the Passover celebration. But, his plans were thwarted because all the believers gathered together in unified prayer (see Acts 12:3–10).

And they had already lost one of their main antagonists for the believers not too long ago when Saul had been converted on the road to Damascus (see Acts 9:1–9). Maybe they were trying to get me out into the open by myself and then kill me. I would not put it past those who hate what we are doing to resort to that type of strategy; they had already tried to do so in the past.

But I had already made the decision that I will always proclaim the good news of Jesus to anyone anywhere. My life is not my own—it is in God's hands. I am willing to die for what I know is true. I had come to realize that even during the more than three years that I had traveled with Jesus there were times that I tended to follow Him at a distance, even while I was with Him! I think that it is safe to say that all of us disciples did that at times; we wanted to believe, but we still at times had our doubts; and if we were honest, we also had our fears. Maybe we were still like that man who, after several of us disciples had prayed for him and nothing happened, brought his son to Jesus to be healed (see Mark 9:14–27). Jesus asked him: "Do you believe?" His answer was what we all have experienced at times: "Yes I believe! Help me with my unbelief!" I think we have all said that in the past. "Help me with my unbelief." But now, after seeing Jesus arisen from the dead, I will never again doubt who He is!

Having said this, I also have to say all I needed to do was remember the vision I just had less than thirty minutes before that. Everything that I saw in the vision came to pass within the hour. The Spirit assured me that I should go with them to meet this centurion named Cornelius. If the Holy Spirit was leading me to what would ultimately be my death, then so be it. I was prepared for God to be glorified in my life or in my death; either way, God would receive all glory. I understand now that I am only a vessel that God will use to reach others.

Luke also asked me why six fellow believers traveled with me to Caesarea: were they afraid for my safety? What was their purpose? Were they prepared to protect me, or what? At the time I didn't really think about why they felt the need to go with me. Maybe they did go with me to offer some protection or maybe just to be with me for encouragement. I'm not really sure. I had never really given that too much thought.

But now that Luke has asked me that question perhaps one of the main reasons they were with me had to do with when I went to Jerusalem after my meeting with Cornelius. The leaders of the Church had a lot of questions about why I went into the home of a Gentile to preach the good news of Jesus's Resurrection. I was able to tell them that the six brethren who had been with me at Caesarea (and who were with me there at Jerusalem) were able to confirm the salvation of Cornelius and his entire household that day.

And I really want to point out the "atmosphere" that I sensed at the meeting with the leaders in Jerusalem. I understood their concern about me going to a Gentile home to share the good news about Jesus; I would have asked the same questions that they asked if it had been one of them that met with Cornelius. The reason I say atmosphere is because I would have to admit that I was probably more concerned about my meeting with the leadership of the Church than I was with my meeting with Cornelius. After all, I had previously been confronted by the Jewish religious leaders. The Jewish leaders were doing everything they could to shut us up so we would stop proclaiming the good news of Jesus's Resurrection. They wanted this message about Jesus to cease and desist.

But then I told the leaders of our movement about how the Holy Spirit had sent me to Cornelius and how the angel had appeared to Cornelius and told him to send for me, and even told him where I was staying. I told them that he and everyone present received the message of salvation, and also the gift of the Holy Spirit as promised by Jesus to all believers. It was at that point that they became quiet and praised God for including all men of any and all backgrounds in those who could be saved. This experience with the leadership of the Church was so much different from the meeting with the temple leadership. But for the grace of God, I could have been killed by those other leaders.

Anyway, back to the men who were sent by Cornelius. Since they did not insist on leaving right away to get back to Caesarea and were willing to lodge with us that night, it helped me to feel a little more comfortable about traveling with them. They were not in any extreme hurry to get me out of Joppa. We were able to talk a little that evening about Cornelius, and though they were not able to tell me a great deal about why he wanted me there, I was able to become more confident about the whole situation. They seemed to be men who were very sincere about this trip they had made to meet with me.

The next day as we left Caesarea, I sensed no danger as we traveled with these men. In fact, they reminded me that since they had orders from Cornelius—who was a centurion—there would be no one detaining us for questioning; all they would have to do was show the orders from Cornelius. What a great way to travel!

Discussion Questions

1. If you were to write a book about what God has done in your life, what three things would you include first?

_____

_____

_____

_____

2. Peter could look on his past and see how God had been preparing him for future service. Can you look back and see things in your past that you didn't understand at the time that have prepared you for today? Would it be beneficial to write them down to remember them in the future?

_____

_____

_____

_____

3. What happened in the Church after James died that may have made a difference in Peter being rescued from his imprisonment?

_____

_____

_____

_____

CHAPTER 7

Peter Meets Cornelius

And the following day they entered Caesarea. Now Cornelius was waiting for them, and had called together his relatives and close friends. As Peter was coming in, Cornelius met him and fell down at his feet and worshiped him. But Peter lifted him up, saying, "Stand up; I myself am also a man." And as he talked with him, he went in and found many who had come together. Then he said to them, "You know how unlawful it is for a Jewish man to keep company with or go to one of another nation. But God has shown me that I should not call any man common or unclean. Therefore I came without objection as soon as I was sent for. I ask, then, for what reason have you sent for me?"

So Cornelius said, "Four days ago I was fasting until this hour; and at the ninth hour I prayed in my house, and behold, a man stood before me in bright clothing, and said, 'Cornelius, your prayer has been heard, and your alms are remembered in the sight of God. Send therefore to Joppa and call Simon here, whose surname is Peter. He is lodging in the house of Simon, a tanner, by the sea. When he comes, he will speak to you.' So I sent to you immediately, and you have done well to come. Now therefore, we are all present before God, to hear all the things commanded you by God (Acts 10:24–33).

Peter's Account

The only delay we experienced was that it was about thirty-eight miles from Joppa to Caesarea, so we had to stop after about twenty-five miles to rest for the night. We arrived at Cornelius's home at about three in the afternoon (the ninth hour) on the second day, so we felt that we had made good time in our travels.

The first thing Cornelius did when I arrived was to bow down before me as if he was worshipping me. That obviously caught me by surprise. So, I lifted him up and told him there was no reason to worship me—I am just a man like he is. There is nothing I have done to deserve any worship from anyone. As we walked

Not knowing quite where or how to start, and only having talked to Cornelius for a few minutes at the entryway to his home, I thought it best to start with what I knew, and what I was in the process of learning about what God was trying to teach me.

into his home still talking, I was amazed at how many people were there in his home waiting for us.

My six companions and I were the only Jews in the house, which at first seemed very uncomfortable for all of us. But they all seemed to be so very gracious and thankful that we had come. And then I (and my six companions) were all reminded by the Spirit that we had been sent there by the vision that I had received.

Not knowing quite where or how to start, and only having talked to Cornelius for a few minutes at the entryway to his home, I thought it best to start with what I knew, and what I was in the process of learning about what God was trying to teach me. It was unlawful for a Jewish man to keep company with someone who was not a Jew (though I am beginning to wonder where that law had originated). God was now showing me that I should not call anyone unclean or unworthy because God was willing to accept anyone that would believe in Him. The thought occurred to me: *I wonder if Cornelius even knew that I was a Jew when he sent for me?*

Anyway, since the arrival of his men to my lodging happened so quickly after my vision had ended, I felt it was important to go there as soon as possible. So I said to him: "*…. for what reason have you sent for me?*" (Acts10:29b).

His answer seemed strange to me! He said that four days before my arrival he had been fasting and praying, and a man in bright clothing had appeared to him and told him: "*Cornelius, your prayer has been heard, and your alms are remembered in the sight of God*" (Acts10:31b). Evidently, God will give visions and dreams to other people—not just Jewish people.

And the details that God was willing to give to him were amazing. Cornelius knew my name was Simon Peter because of the vision he had received. Simon was my given name from birth and Peter was the name that Jesus said I would be known by. He also knew that I was in the city of Joppa, and that I was staying in the home of Simon, who was a tanner. He was also told that when I arrived, I would share with him what he needed to know—more specifically, what he should do. It was obvious that he did not care that I was a Jew, and he thanked me for coming so quickly. He said he and his family and friends were all ready to hear whatever it was I needed to share with them. Something so important that he was sure was going to make a difference in his life.

++++++++++++++++++++++++++++++++

Cornelius's Account

It was with great wonder and anticipation that I waited for my servants and soldier to return with this man named Simon Peter. I was thankful that I had chosen to send Julius—my most dependable soldier—with my two servants. He was a man I would trust with my children, and I was confident he would waste no time in returning.

Yet, it had become hard to focus on anything else since I had the visit from the angel of God; I had no idea what to expect. I wasn't sure if it was a good idea to do this, but because of my excitement and anticipation, and the fact that I couldn't seem to think or talk about anything else for those four days, I ended up inviting all my friends and family to my home. I wanted them to hear firsthand what this man was going to tell me. I just thought that if he was going to tell me what I needed to do, then it would probably be beneficial for everyone else—they should probably do the same thing that I needed to do.

On that fourth day I started thinking more about what the angel had said: *"Your prayers and your alms have come up for a memorial before God"* (Acts10:4b). What was it about my prayers that had such an impact on this God I was praying to that He would send an angel to tell me what I must do? None of the gods I used to pray to ever did something like that for me; the fact of the matter is I never got the impression that any of those gods ever heard my prayers, much less gave an answer.

What was it about my prayers that had such an impact on this God I was praying to that He would send an angel to tell me what I must do?

So, what was it about my prayers that made such an impact on this God I was praying to? Perhaps the reason I was praying to this God was because of all the interest that had been generated these past few years in this God of Israel, mainly due to what had happened to Jesus in Jerusalem. This God called Jehovah had quite a way of making His presence known sometimes. I knew some things about the history of the Jewish people; at one time in their past, they had been in slavery in the land of Egypt (see Exodus 1). Somehow these people came up with the idea to tell the pharaoh at the time that they wanted to leave Egypt and no longer serve him there. That obviously was not a well-received idea. The pharaoh absolutely forbade it—and then made the conditions of their slavery even worse for them.

I don't really know a great deal more about how they ended up getting out of Egypt—since I am not a Jew—but I have heard through historical accounts that when the pharaoh decided to let them leave that he changed his mind and tried to go get them and make them return. That did not go well for him; he and his army and all his horses drowned in the Red Sea, but somehow all the Israelite people who were on foot managed to cross the Red Sea without incident (see Exodus 14). I always thought that the story sounded pretty farfetched, but the story could have been easily disproved if the pharaoh, who supposedly died in the sea, would have stepped up and said it was all a lie—that he had actually let them go because he was such a nice guy. But that doesn't really sound like something a king would say or do, especially one of the pharaohs.

Again, what was it about my prayers that made such an impact on this God I was praying to? What was it that I would need to do? It was obvious to me that it was something very important, but I just could not yet fathom what it might be. So, if this man named Simon Peter had the answer to my prayers then maybe he was more than just a man? I was thankful that I had thought about this before he arrived; if he was a god or an angel then I should bow before him in worship when he arrived. I certainly did not want to make him angry when he was coming to help me know what I needed to do.

So that is what I did! When he arrived that afternoon, I met him at the door and bowed before him in worship. But he took me by the hand, helped me up, and said to me; *"Stand up; I myself am also a man!"* (Acts 10:26b). There is no reason to worship me. We stood there at the entryway to my home and talked for several minutes and then I invited him into my home. He seemed quite surprised to see so many people in my home; I hoped that I did not offend him by having so many people there.

He started by explaining how it was not normally acceptable for a Jewish man to be in the home of someone who was not Jewish. The thought of offending him in this way never even crossed my mind; I probably should have met him outside somewhere. I wondered if that would have been more acceptable. But, he calmed my fears by saying that God had been showing him that he should be more accepting of others and to not call them common or unclean. Though, at the time, I wasn't entirely sure what he meant by that. *Did the Jewish people really believe that all other peoples and nations were unclean?* I wondered.

God must have really been working on Peter before he came to meet with me, especially when I learned that he was actually a Jew and was staying with someone who made his living as a tanner. If the Jewish people had the habit of labeling people as unclean then certainly they would have seen Simon the tanner as unclean. If he wasn't supposed to go into my home because I was unclean, surely he would have not been allowed to go into the home of someone who was a tanner of animal hides. There is so much I have never quite understood about the Jewish people; sometimes I get the impression that they don't fully understand themselves or their religion either.

And then he surprised me with a question: "*…..I came without objection as soon as I was sent for. I ask, then, for what reason have you sent for me?*" (Acts10:29b) The reason this surprised me was that I thought he would know why I sent for him. I was the one who needed to know what to do, and he was the one who knew what it was I needed to do. So, I told him about my vision from four days ago, and how the man (or angel) had said that my prayers had been heard and my alms had been remembered in the sight of God.

It was then that Peter's face seemed to go through myriad expressions—surprise, uncertainty, puzzlement, confusion, bewilderment; but then it suddenly changed to excitement, confidence, and certainty. It was like he suddenly knew exactly what he needed to tell me. He knew what I needed to know and do.

++++++++++++++++++++++++++++++++

LUKE INTERJECTS

At this point in the story, Peter told me how surprised he so often is when opportunities arise to share the good news of Jesus with people who do not yet know the gospel message. It seemed that in this particular encounter he would not need to do any convincing to Cornelius about the message he had to share. It seemed that God, through His Holy Spirit, had already prepared him beyond his wildest imagination. The only unusual thing he had to do was tell Cornelius not to bow down to him in worship; another person bowing to him was a new thing that he had not yet dealt with. Hopefully, it would never happen again. He felt uncomfortable with someone bowing to him.

Peter also suggested that it might be of some benefit to record all the different ways the Holy Spirit works on the hearts of men to prepare them for the message of the gospel. My thought was that we might be able to learn several ways the Spirit works on the hearts of people, but I don't think there is any way we could learn all the different ways He works in men's hearts. But it was certainly a novel idea. I'm just not sure anyone could ever achieve such a momentous task.

Discussion Questions

1. How long do you think Cornelius had been praying when the angel appeared to him? Think of examples from Scripture of people who have prayed for long periods of time about something important to them. Do you have something in your life that you have been praying about for a long time that still has not been answered? What can we learn from these examples?

_____

_____

_____

_____

2. What do you think it was that Peter was supposed to tell Cornelius about what he needed to do?

_____

_____

_____

_____

3. Why is it so common for us to have doubts when we have an opportunity to share the gospel with someone?

CHAPTER 8

Peter Continues

It was at this point that this whole venture to meet with Cornelius began to make sense. I now knew what the message was that I needed to tell Cornelius, which was Luke's second question! All this time since my vision of the large sheet coming down from heaven, my travel from Joppa to Caesarea with the soldier and Cornelius's servants, and even when I met him at his entryway, I have been wondering how I was going to share with him the Good News of Jesus. I was certain that God had arranged this opportunity to meet with this centurion, but I was not entirely sure what this man was expecting from me. I knew that since God was directing my steps, then He had a plan so I could share the gospel with this man; I just was not sure how that was going to happen.

But then again doubt came to my mind: were his intentions really to learn more about Jesus? Or was he intending to turn me over to the authorities that were trying to stop the spread of the gospel? Once again, I had to remind myself of the vision I had two days ago, when the angel told me to go with these men and meet with Cornelius.

But still, how was I to start telling a Roman soldier—a centurion none-the-less—what he needed to do? Yet, God, by His Holy Spirit, had already prepared this man for what needed to be done. Here was a man that had heard all the stories about Jesus's death and Resurrection but had never really personalized all the events he had heard about; he didn't yet know how all of this actually applied to him.

So I began: *"…. In truth I perceive that God shows no partiality. But in every nation whoever fears Him and works righteousness is accepted by Him. The word which God sent to the children of Israel, preaching peace through Jesus Christ—He is Lord of all—that word you know, which was proclaimed throughout all Judea, and began from Galilee after the baptism which John preached: how God anointed Jesus of Nazareth with the Holy Spirit and with power, who went about doing good and healing all who were oppressed by the devil, for God was with Him. And we are witnesses of all things which He did both in the land of the Jews and in Jerusalem whom they killed by hanging Him on a tree. Him God raised up on the third day, and showed Him openly, not to all the people, but to witnesses chosen before by God, even to us who ate and drank with Him after He arose from the dead. And He commanded us to preach to the people, and to testify that it is He who was ordained by God to be Judge of the living and the dead. To Him all the prophets witness that, through His name, whoever believes in Him will receive remission of sins"* (Acts 10:34b–43).

Cornelius, we as the Jewish nation have always understood that we are God's chosen people; but evidently we have not completely understood what that actually meant. We are not His chosen people because He loves us more than any other people; we are His chosen people because of His special covenant He made with Abraham, Isaac, and Jacob (whose name God changed to Israel—that is why we are called Israelites). But there is more to being His chosen people than we ever realized. We are His chosen people so He can bring salvation to all the world, and that salvation is only made possible through faith in the finished work of Jesus the Christ.

There are those who choose to continue remaining in the Old Covenant with the imperfect sacrificial system. They are missing out on the New Covenant that has been established by the death of our perfect sacrificial Lamb, JESUS. Our mindset for all our lives was that God would send our deliverer to free us from slavery to Rome, or to Babylon, or to the Medes and Persians, or even to Egypt. What Jesus came to do was to free us from the power and bondage of sin. We, like all of mankind, have been slaves to our own sinful nature—ever since the fall of Adam and Eve.

In fact, anyone who chooses to believe they can be in right standing with God because of the "good things" they do will be in for a sad surprise.

In fact, anyone who chooses to believe they can be in right standing with God because of the "good things" they do will be in for a sad surprise.

All of our lives we, as God's chosen people, have always understood that the sacrifices we offered continually for our sins was not adequate. It was only a temporary solution. We knew that a more perfect sacrifice would be needed; and God, by His grace and mercy, has provided that sacrifice by His Son Jesus.

Jesus lived a perfect, sinless life so that He could become our perfect sacrifice so that we would not have to always be wondering if we are in right standing with God because of some sin we committed that we have not yet asked forgiveness for. Or wonder if our good deeds "outweigh' any sins we have committed? We no longer need to sacrifice a lamb, or goat, or bull, or dove, or any such animal to receive forgiveness because Jesus covered it all by dying as the perfect sacrifice for all of our sins and disobedience.

He came to establish a better covenant with us and all men everywhere—not just the Jewish people. This new covenant that Jesus has brought about through His perfect sacrifice provides us with forgiveness of our sin and power over sin. His sacrifice is the sacrifice we all need, and His sacrifice is now the only sacrifice we will ever need. There is no other sacrifice we will ever need to be in right standing with God.

In fact, "…. *in every nation whoever fears Him and works righteousness is accepted by Him*" (Acts 10:35). We also understand now that God shows no partiality to any particular people or person. Anyone that calls on the name of the Lord can (and will) be saved.

Cornelius, I believe you understand that your good works cannot save you, just as we have always known that following the Law to the letter was still lacking something. The lack of peace that you are experiencing is due to the fact that you have not yet received the salvation and right standing with God that can be yours just by accepting that God has made it all attainable by the work that Jesus accomplished on the Cross. He died not only for the sins of Israel. He died for the sins of all of mankind, including you, for anyone who calls on the name of the Lord!

++

CORNELIUS CONTINUES

As Simon Peter began talking to us I sensed a feeling of excitement and peace—excitement that had been building for the past four days; but also peace, though I wasn't quite sure why I felt this surge of peace. I wasn't even aware that I was lacking peace until that moment. I was beginning to realize that all the things I had been doing these past several months were important for me to do, but none of them helped me to be in right standing with God. There was still something I had been missing.

Simon Peter said many things to us over the next several minutes, but what caught my attention the most was when he said that Jesus suffered and died on the cross, He did it for all of mankind, including me. No one, not even the Jewish people who were present here with us, had ever been able to be in right standing with God based on the good things they did. How could a man

> **But Peter was helping me to understand that Jesus lived and died as a man so that we (including me) could have forgiveness of all our past sins against God.**

born in sin ever do enough good things to stand in the presence of a Holy God? But Peter was helping me to understand that Jesus lived and died as a man so that we (including me) could have forgiveness of all our past sins against God.

Because of my concern for my family and friends who were there with us, and wondering what they were thinking about what Peter was saying, I kind of stole a glance at several of them. Everyone seemed to be listening intently; he had the attention of everyone.

And when he said: "*.... whoever believes in Him will receive remission of sins*" (Acts10:43b) it was like something happened that I can't explain. I felt like this was a moment of great importance; a moment where I needed to make an important decision. I was beginning to understand that Jesus did more than just die for the sin of all men; He died for me! Was I willing to put my trust in Him? Was I willing to put my faith in Him? Did I want to keep on trying to do enough good things to receive this gift of peace and right standing with God, or would I choose to put my faith and trust in this Jesus, who not only died on a cross but also arose from the dead. Many were putting their faith and trust in Jesus. Was I willing to do so too?

As soon as I said, "YES!" it was like everyone else there came to the same decision. But, something else also happened that I did not really understand at the time, though Peter and the men with him seemed to understand.

DISCUSSION QUESTIONS

1. When are the works we do important in God's plan of salvation? The answer we often give is that they are not important to our salvation. But, are our works ever important to someone else's salvation? If so, in what way?

2. Cornelius's story reveals to us that it is possible to know all about the story of Jesus without really knowing Him for who He is. There are many in the world today who claim to know Him, but their lives do not reflect the peace that comes from being in right relationship with Him. How many people do you know that might benefit from hearing His story?

3. You may have noticed some repetition of doubts or questions in Peter's account of the story. Do you believe that would be a common occurrence for Peter? Why or why not? Have you ever experienced a repetition of doubts or questions as Peter may have done in this story? Why or why not?

_____

_____

_____

_____

CHAPTER 9

The Holy Spirit Falls on the Gentiles

While Peter was still speaking these words, the Holy Spirit fell upon all those who heard the word. And those of the circumcision who believed were astonished, as many as came with Peter, because the gift of the Holy Spirit had been poured out on the Gentiles also. For they heard them speak with tongues and magnify God.

Then Peter answered, "Can anyone forbid water, that these should not be baptized who have received the Holy Spirit just as we have?" And he commanded them to be baptized in the name of the Lord. Then they asked him to stay a few days (Acts 10:44-48).

CORNELIUS CONTINUES

While Peter was still speaking to us, it seemed like everyone who was there started speaking; but none of what was being said by any of us was understandable. Though none of what we were saying made sense, it still "felt" right—if I can use that word. We spoke these unintelligible words for several minutes, and then Peter spoke up. What he said was that our response of speaking those words helped to confirm for him that we had become believers. We had received the gift of the Holy Spirit and had spoken in tongues. It was the promised Holy Spirit that Jesus had told them would come to dwell in the believers after He ascended into heaven (see John 14:16–17, 23, 26; 15:26; 16:7, 13). Evidently, the Holy Spirit will dwell within all believers, not just the disciples.

At that point, Peter told us that we should be baptized in water. We were new to this, so he had to explain to us the purpose of being baptized in water. The joy and peace we were experiencing was such that we all wanted to be obedient, so we readily agreed and were baptized that same evening.

++++++++++++++++++++++++++++++++

Luke Comments

Peter, I think I am beginning to understand something you said at the council meeting in Jerusalem a few years ago when you had to explain why you were even there at the home of Cornelius. You had said to them: *"If therefore God gave them the same gift as He gave us when we believed on the Lord Jesus Christ, who was I that I could withstand God?"* (see Acts 11:17). Just going there and sharing the gospel message with Cornelius's household would not have been enough proof to the Jerusalem Council that they had become believers.

When they received the Holy Spirit, as you had done, it was obvious that they had all become believers. How could you object to their newfound faith, since they had received the Holy Spirit in the same manner in which you received on the Day of Pentecost? How could you object to their newfound faith? How could anyone deny they had received the Holy Spirit when they spoke in tongues as you and others have done since the day of Pentecost?

Sometimes, I wish I could have been present with you in that upper room in Jerusalem when you were waiting for the Holy Spirit to come as Jesus promised would happen after He ascended into heaven. I think you said you were waiting there in prayer for about ten days. Then the Day of Pentecost arrived, and everyone present was filled with the Holy Spirit. The first evidence of you all being filled with the Spirit was that everyone spoke in tongues. Was your experience that day any different from other times since then when others have been filled with the Holy Spirit?

++++++++++++++++++++++++++++++

Peter Continues

Yes, Luke! I think that you just answered your third question: "How did I know Cornelius had become a believer?" There have been several occasions now when I or one of the other disciples has led someone to receive Christ as their Lord and Savior. It seems that each time God has granted the gift of the Holy Spirit to each new believer which is what Jesus told us would happen in His last week before He was crucified (see John 15:7–8). The way each new believer has been assured of their salvation, and the way we, the ones praying with them, have been assured, is that they receive the Holy Spirit. And, obviously, the way we know that they have received the Holy Spirit is when they begin to speak in tongues. The question that we should ask, though, is, *"Does every person who receives the Holy Spirit speak in tongues?"*

These new believers will all need to have some understanding of what Jesus taught us about the Holy Spirit. I know that Matthew and John are both already working on writing out many things that they have experienced and recorded while we lived and traveled with Jesus during those three years. And now, Luke, you are doing the same, though you weren't with us during that last week. I am sure that at least one of them will have a great deal to share about that time when Jesus told us of the coming Holy Spirit during His last week with us.

> **These new believers will all need to have some understanding of what Jesus taught us about the Holy Spirit.**

But again, is our experience with the Holy Spirit filling us as He has done thus far the same in every situation? Should we expect the same experience in every account?

I know that when we first received the Holy Spirit in the upper room in Jerusalem everyone present received the Holy Spirit and everyone spoke in tongues (see Acts 2:4).

After that, when John and I were arrested and questioned by the Sanhedrin Council for healing the paralytic man at the temple gate called Beautiful (see Acts 3:2), we spoke with great boldness to the leadership there. They were amazed by our boldness and understanding of Scripture and how we proclaimed with confidence that Jesus was raised from the dead. I think that they were aware that we were not what anyone would consider "learned scholars", but they were not able to refute us. The only thing they could attribute our knowledge and understanding to was that we had learned so much from our time with Jesus (see Acts 4:13). When they released us, we went back to where the other believers were at and told them of how God had given us success in our encounter with the Jewish leaders. We praised God together and prayed that God would continue to give all of us believers boldness to speak His Word (see Acts 4:29). When we prayed, everyone was once again filled with the Holy Spirit and began to speak the Word of God with boldness (see Acts 4:31).

On another occasion, while we were all still in Jerusalem, we learned that many in Samaria had received the Gospel message. Philip, who was one of the original seven deacons chosen to serve in Jerusalem, was the one who had gone to Samaria to share the Gospel there not long after the death of Stephen. Those people of Samaria had believed Philip's message and were baptized, but they did not receive the Holy Spirit at that time. So John and I were sent there to lay hands on them to pray that they might receive the Holy Spirit. When they received the Spirit, Simon the sorcerer—who had also become a believer—asked us to give him the power also to lay hands on others so that they could also receive the Holy Spirit. Of course we rebuked him for his request because he thought that he could buy this power or ability to give the Holy Spirit to others (see Acts 8:15–25). We told him he needed to repent of his wicked thoughts and ask God for forgiveness and he asked us to pray for him that his heart would be changed.

After that Philip met an Ethiopian eunuch who had gone to Jerusalem to worship and was returning to his homeland in his chariot. He was able to strike up a conversation with the eunuch about a passage in Isaiah the man had been reading (see Acts 8:35–39). When the eunuch confessed his faith in Christ as the Son of God, Stephen baptized him in water.

I also remember that when Saul was converted after his experience on the road to Damascus (see Acts 9:1–19), a disciple there at Damascus by the name of Ananias went and laid his hands on Saul and prayed for him. Saul had become a believer because of the experience he had on the road to Damascus but had become blind because of the experience. The disciple named Ananias prayed for him to receive his sight and be filled with the Holy Spirit. After that, he went and was baptized.

What can we learn so far from these examples of new believers being saved and of them receiving the Holy Spirit and speaking in tongues? It seems to me that the Holy Spirit is much like Jesus always was with us when He was with us for those three years. We always wanted Jesus to do things a certain way so we could have a pattern to follow, so we could know how to do it. In my mind I think, *Since Jesus did it this way, then I will do it that way also.* I think it is kind of like trying to put Him in a box, but He won't fit in a box. Plus, who wants to serve a God that you can fit into a box? That would be like telling Him He can do this but He can't do that! That has never worked very well for any of us. I pray that we never try to do that with the Holy Spirit.

Aside from the wonderful teaching we received from our time with Jesus, it was always exciting when someone would come to Him with a question or just to make a statement. He seldom responded the same way twice, but He always gave an answer that astounded all of us. If someone was desiring healing, He always performed the healing in a different way. That's what makes following Him exciting; we never know what to expect!

If Jesus can't be put in a box, why would we want to put the Holy Spirit in a box? It would certainly limit Him, and it would limit us because Jesus said we would do even greater things (see John 14:12) than He did, which is really hard to comprehend still.

Discussion Questions

1. What was it that Simon the sorcerer saw that excited him so much (Acts 8) that made him want to buy the power to lay hands on others so they could receive the Holy Spirit?

2. In Acts 9, how would Ananias know that Saul had received the Holy Spirit?

3. How important do you believe the gift of the Holy Spirit should be in our lives today? Should speaking in tongues be part of our prayer lives today? Why or why not?

_____

_____

_____

_____

CHAPTER 10

Paul Meets With the Jerusalem Council

"Now the apostles and brethren who were in Judea heard that the Gentiles had also received the word of God. And when Peter came up to Jerusalem, those of the circumcision contended with him, saying, "You went in to uncircumcised men and ate with them!"

But Peter explained it to them in order from the beginning, saying: "I was in the city of Joppa praying; and in a trance I saw a vision, an object descending like a great sheet, let down from heaven by four corners; and it came to me. When I observed it intently and considered, I saw four-footed animals of the earth, wild beasts, creeping things, and birds of the air. And I heard a voice saying to me, 'Rise, Peter; kill and eat.'

But I said, 'Not so, Lord! For nothing common or unclean has at any time entered my mouth.' But the *voice answered me again from heaven, 'What God has cleansed you must not call common.' Now this was done three times, and all were drawn up again into heaven. At that very moment, three men stood before the house where I was, having been sent to me from Caesarea. Then the Spirit told me to go with them, doubting nothing. Moreover these six brethren accompanied me, and we entered the man's house. And he told us how he had seen an angel standing in his house, who said to him, 'Send men to Joppa, and call for Simon whose surname is Peter, who will tell you words by which you and all your household will be saved.'*

And as I began to speak, the Holy Spirit fell upon them, as upon us at the beginning. Then I remembered the word of the Lord, how He said, 'John indeed baptized with water, but you shall be baptized with the Holy Spirit.' If therefore God gave them the same gift as He gave us when we believed on the Lord Jesus Christ, who was I that I could withstand God?" When they heard these things they became silent; and they glorified God, saying, "Then God has also granted to the Gentiles repentance to life." (Acts 11:1–18)

Luke Continues

It certainly was rewarding to meet with you several months ago, Peter, when we first talked about your meeting with the Jerusalem Council and your meeting with Cornelius. Also, the time I personally spent with Cornelius was valuable. Both of you have inspired me in my faith. It is hard to imagine anything more exciting than following the Lord and being led by the Spirit as you have been. I am looking forward to hearing more from others as I am able to meet with them. But I felt for now it would be helpful to come back again to meet with you and talk some more about your meeting with the Jerusalem Council. Also if you have thought of anything you would like to add to what we have already recorded last time we were together, then we could do so now.

> **It is hard to imagine anything more exciting than following the Lord and being led by the Spirit as you have been.**

++++++++++++++++++++++++++++

Peter Continues

Well Luke, I have to say that when you first came to see me several months ago, I wasn't sure it would be worth your time or mine to talk about my meeting with Cornelius. But, since we have started reminiscing about how God was at work at that time in both my life and Cornelius's life, I have to admit that it has been refreshing for me to revisit that period of time. Sometimes we forget about the great things God has done. I don't like to dwell on the past, whether it be the bad things or the good things that have happened. I am always trying to look for what God is wanting to do in and through me today, not just what He did yesterday.

But, your desire to learn and record some of the things God is doing and has done in the lives of His followers has been inspiring for me. It makes me think that perhaps I should start writing down some of the things that God has shown me; perhaps it could be helpful for future generations, if the Lord should delay His Return.

One thing I am grateful for when I think about going to meet with Cornelius was the fact that I took those six Jewish brethren with me. They were all recent converts from Joppa, and it was a time for great growth for each of them. Since then, they have all continued growing in their faith, and I believe God will continue to use them to further His work there in Joppa.

Since I went to Jerusalem soon after meeting with Cornelius, I was thankful that those six brethren traveled with me for those several weeks. They were especially helpful to me when I met in Jerusalem with the leaders of the Church there. By the time we arrived in Jerusalem all the apostles and other leaders already knew about our meeting with Cornelius. And they certainly had a lot of questions for me. But I have to remind myself that if it had been one of them who met with Cornelius, I would have had a lot of questions for them too. Having those six brethren with me at Jerusalem certainly made it easier for everyone involved in that discussion to accept what God was and is doing.

I already told you earlier about how different it was being questioned by the leaders of the Church and the time John and I were questioned by the leaders of the Jewish temple. And you already know that Stephen has been stoned by those religious leaders for preaching, and James (the brother of John) was killed by King Herod. Though the leaders of our movement to preach Jesus had questions for me about Cornelius they evidently kept their minds and hearts open to hear what I had to say, which was quite different from the religious leaders at the temple in Jerusalem.

Now that I have had time to think about it, I find it intriguing that the first outside group to receive the Gospel were the Samaritans. But, then again, when Jesus told us to wait in the upper room for the promised Holy Spirit, He told us we should be witnesses first in Jerusalem, then in Judea and Samaria, and to the end of the earth. So, I should not be surprised it happened in that order. The Samaritans are a mixed race, made up of people from the Northern Kingdom tribes who intermarried with people who had been relocated there by the of king of Assyria. The Assyrian king had relocated most of the people from the tribes of Israel who comprised the Northern Kingdom, but he had left a remnant of Israelites in the land.

Because of what many might call a feud between the Samaritans and us, who were mostly of the Southern Kingdom, we had to remind ourselves that Jesus actually took us through Samaria one time so He could preach the good news to that Samaritan woman.

Aside from that, it was Philip the deacon who actually went to Samaria to preach the Gospel, and many there heard and received his message.

Sometimes, I look back and reflect on what we were like before Jesus came, even before we were divided into the Northern and Southern Kingdoms. We were very sure of ourselves because we knew we were God's chosen people. Though we only had three kings before we divided into two kingdoms—King Saul, King David, and King Solomon—those certainly had to have been our greatest days.

Then I am reminded of what Moses told our descendants while they were still wandering in the desert. *"Do not think in your heart, after the Lord your God has cast them out before you, saying, 'Because of my righteousness the Lord has brought me in to possess this land'; but it is because of the wickedness of these nations that the Lord is driving them out from before you. It is not because of your righteousness or the uprightness of your heart that you go in to possess their land, but because of the wickedness of these nations that the LORD your God drives them out from before you, and that He may fulfill the word which the Lord swore to your fathers, to Abraham, Isaac, and Jacob. Therefore understand that the Lord your God is not giving you this good land to possess because of your righteousness, for you are a stiff-necked people"* (Deuteronomy 9:4–6).

> **Sometimes, I look back and reflect on what we were like before Jesus came, even before we were divided into the Northern and Southern Kingdoms.**

On more than one occasion in our history, God came close to destroying our people; the only thing that held Him back was His covenant that He had made with Abraham, Isaac, and Jacob, and the intercession of Moses and other leaders.

It seems that everything that has happened in our past has been leading up to us realizing that it was not possible for us to live our lives in such a way that God would accept us as righteous in His sight. We would need help, and that help came from the life, death, and resurrection of Jesus Christ, the Son of the Living God. We would need His perfect sacrifice for our sin. Thankfully, Cornelius also came to that understanding. Though he was a good man, well respected by everyone (including the Jewish people), he had not experienced the peace of God that only comes from having our sins forgiven.

I am thankful for the many Jewish people who have become believers these past several years. I am also thankful that God has included Gentiles into His fold! And I am eternally grateful that He chose me to help bring the message of salvation to the lost and dying in all the world. And when I am gone, I know of at least six other believers who will carry on in my place.

As more of us who call ourselves disciples and followers of Christ catch the vision of what God wants to do in and through us, I believe we will see the message of Jesus spread throughout the world. He has commissioned us to, *"Go therefore and make disciples of all the nations, baptizing them in the name of the Father and of the Son and of the Holy Spirit, teaching them to observe all things that I have commanded you; and lo, I am with you always, even to the end of the age"* (Matthew 28:19–20).

My prayer is that it will happen soon!

Discussion Questions

1. If you were Luke, what questions would you have for Peter about his encounter with Cornelius? Are there other questions you might have for him?

2. What was the reason the Assyrian king relocated most of the Israelites of the Northern Kingdom to other parts of the world? Why did God allow it to happen?

3. What was the difference between the works that Cornelius did before his meeting with Peter, and the works that he did after their meeting? Why are the works we do today after we become believers important?

_____

_____

_____

_____

CHAPTER 11

More Conversation Between Luke and Peter

LUKE: I learned recently that Cornelius, his family, and his household servants are all growing in their faith and are making a difference in the lives of the people of Caesarea. I also learned that some of the soldiers who have served under him, who have committed their lives to Christ, are being transferred to other ports and stations.

I know specifically that Julius—the soldier that traveled to Joppa with the two servants to get you and take you to Cornelius—is being reassigned to what is known as the Augustan Regiment (see Acts 27:1). His duties will include, obviously, the protection of the emperor. From what I understand, he requested this new assignment because it includes the transfer of prisoners to Rome. He believes that prisoners need to hear the gospel as much as anyone else—and perhaps they are at a place in their lives now where they will more readily receive the message of forgiveness. So, he wants to do whatever he can to share the gospel with whoever will listen.

So many good things have happened in Caesarea because of Cornelius's conversion. So many Gentiles—and Roman soldiers—are choosing to follow Jesus Christ. I am always so amazed at how so many are sharing their newfound faith with others. My prayer is that that never ends.

Sometimes, I ask myself questions about all that has happened in our lifetimes.

One question I often think about is this: *What would have happened if Cornelius chose not to believe what you told him he needed to do? What if he decided that since every other god he knew of required him to do certain things, he would just keep on trying to earn his right standing with God?*

> **What would have happened if Cornelius chose not to believe what you told him he needed to do?**

PETER: Luke, thank you for telling me about what you have learned about Cornelius and his household and all the soldiers who became believers. I had not heard any of that yet. I have to say, though, Luke, you sure know how to ask a lot of good questions.

It is hard to imagine that anyone who experienced all that Cornelius experienced would be able to walk away and say, "I don't believe!" But, then again, think of all the Jewish people and even the religious leaders who continue to deny everything they saw when Jesus walked among us. They have chosen to continue to trust in their own ability to work for their standing with God. Perhaps they think that because God is a God of love, of mercy, and of grace that He will not condemn them to hell if they do enough good things. They forget that He is also a just God, and to have all those attributes requires that He also be fair.

Perhaps they believe that Jesus is not the Son of God, so they are still looking for the true Messiah to come. I don't know how it is possible for people who saw everything that happened in Jerusalem to walk away and say they don't believe; evidently, they have been blinded to His salvation because of their sin.

Thankfully, Cornelius chose to walk in faith and is continuing to do so! His decision to follow the Lord has made a significant impact for so many others.

LUKE: Peter, as a leader of the Church, and a close disciple of Jesus, are you ever concerned for the new things that God has brought about into this new Church? The Jewish religious leaders have often misunderstood or misinterpreted the scriptures and abused their role as leaders, putting heavy burdens upon the followers that are more than they should have to bear. Are you ever concerned that might happen with the Church now? What can we do to make sure that the Church of the future does not go down the same paths?

PETER: Luke, once again, you have asked some important questions. My prayer is that now that the Holy Spirit lives within each of us believers that we will all stay in tune with what the Lord wants to accomplish in each of us. I believe that if we always take on the mindset of the Lord—which is that of a servant—then we will always be looking out for others first instead of ourselves. This is especially true for those who are leaders. Jesus was the perfect example of what a servant should look like.

Obviously, the easiest way to fall prey to our leaders misinterpreting the Scriptures is to not know the Scriptures ourselves. Every believer will need to study the Word of God themselves so they can rightly teach others and defend the truth. If we as believers know the Word ourselves and speak out against wrong teaching then that will make a huge impact in defending against abuse from leaders. Knowing the truth will set us free! It can also be a huge help to our leaders if others are willing to keep them accountable.

We have already actually experienced some of what you are asking. Now that so many Gentiles are becoming believers, many of the Pharisees who have become believers have been trying to convince us to require all the new Gentile believers to be circumcised. We have addressed the issue already and all are agreed that since circumcision did not save us then why would we want to require it of them? My experience has been that whenever we as men begin to push our own ideas without truly seeking the heart of God then we can expect division and problems. We definitely want to avoid that.

LUKE: What is next for you Peter?

PETER: I believe it is important that I do the work He gave me to do, and that is to feed the flock of God. Sometimes I kind of wrestle with what that actually involves, but I believe part of the answer is that I need to make every effort to strengthen and encourage the brethren. So, I have endeavored to do those very things ever since.

It doesn't matter where I am at or what I have available for me to use. My location makes no difference. I know that wherever I am, I can speak God's love and peace to whoever will listen. If someone is offended by me sharing the gospel then I still know what I am supposed to do. I have learned from sharing the gospel so freely that if someone is offended by me sharing the gospel then at least they have heard it. And that is what is important. My responsibility is to be obedient and trust God for the result.

Isaiah spoke the heart of God when he said: *So shall My word be that goes forth from My mouth; it shall not return to Me void, but it shall accomplish what I please, and it shall prosper in the thing for which I sent it* (see Isaiah 55:11). Either we believe His Word is right or we don't. I am choosing to believe His Word is right!

Luke, having watched you these past few visits as you record the things you are hearing is a great encouragement and example to me. So, I also will be looking for time and opportunity to start writing down things that I believe God would have me share with others. None of us knows how long it will be before Jesus returns for His Church. My hope and prayer is that it will be soon, but until He does return, He has told us to GO and reach as many people with the Gospel as we can. So, that is what I will do. I will keep preaching the Gospel until I die or until He returns! But I also know that writing letters of encouragement and exhortation like you are doing can be very meaningful and helpful to new believers in the cities that have already been reached with the gospel.

LUKE: Thank you, Peter, for your time on this project. You have been very helpful and have given me insight into so many things I was not aware of. Do you have anything else you would like to add? Or do you have any questions for me?

PETER: Well, I can see that you have a lot of work ahead of you, Luke. I would imagine that you will be heading home now, to compile all your new information so future generations can read and benefit from what you have done. After that, what will be next for you? Do you have further plans with your writing?

LUKE: Yes, I may return home to compile all that I have recorded thus far, but I also know that I can do that wherever I am at, so I am considering doing some more traveling. I have thought about spending time with some of the other disciples to hear accounts of what they are doing and that may happen in the future if the Lord tarries His return.

I know that Saul, who wasn't even one of the original disciples, has been traveling with Barnabas for some time, but they recently parted ways. My home is in Antioch in Syria, and I know that he has preached there on more than one occasion. From what I understand, Barnabas took John Mark with him, and they have gone to Cyprus. Saul has recently decided to go by the name of Paul, and his new travelling partner is a man named Silas.

I know that his first journey to share the gospel took him as far as Antioch of Pisidia, and I believe he is wanting to return to the cites he has been to already, but this time I am sure he will want to go much further, perhaps as far as Macedonia. If he is planning to do that, then it would make sense for him to go from Antioch of Pisidia to Troas, which is a port city about four hundred miles to the west. From Troas it is about two days by ship from there to Neapolis and Philippi.

If I travel by ship from Caesarea to Troas, I should arrive there before he is able to make the long journey through the regions of Cilicia, Pisidia, Phrygia, possibly Galatia, and Mysia. I actually have some family living at Troas, so I will be able to stay with them until I learn where he is at. If he is still there preaching the Gospel nearby then he won't be too hard to find. I am sure that if he has already been at Troas then someone will surely know where he went to next.

If he hasn't arrived there yet, I can wait a few days for him; if I have to backtrack toward Antioch, I should be able to do that without too much trouble. I will just have to trust the Lord to direct our paths so we can find each other. Traveling by ship makes more sense than traveling by caravan or by foot if I hope to catch up with him.

PETER: Yes, I would agree it does make sense to do that. Let's pray as we go our separate ways. "Father God, I thank You today for all You continue to do in the lives of those who are committed to serving You. My prayer is that You will continue to lead us and guide us in all that we put our hands to do. May You continue to reveal to us the direction You want us to go each day. May Your hand of protection be upon each of us every day. If Your will is for

Luke to meet up with Paul near Troas, then I pray it will happen without a great deal of difficulty.

As our forefathers have served as examples for us, may the way we live our lives each day be examples for those who will come after us. You have shown us that nothing that comes our way will be more than we can handle when we follow and trust You. Help us to keep our eyes set on You when any difficulty might come our way.

When it comes to temptation that might come our way, we understand that You won't allow a temptation that is more than we can bear. With every temptation, You always provide a way of escape, so we won't fall. Help us to keep our eyes on You, so we will see the way out.

I am thankful, Lord, that You called me to follow You over fifteen years ago when all I really knew was fishing. I was in no way what anyone would have called a Bible scholar. I have learned that there is a difference between knowing Scripture and moving in the power of the Scripture. You told us we would receive that power after You ascended to heaven. That is when the promised Holy Spirit would come upon us and would give us boldness to declare the gospel to any and all. May we learn to walk in the Spirit, so we will not give in to the old fleshly desires. May we learn to walk in that same Spirit, so we can boldly proclaim the message of salvation to a lost and dying world that can be found only by faith in the finished work of our Savior—the Lord Jesus Christ!

Other Scripture passages that will give more insight and understanding into salvation, water baptism, Baptism in the Holy Spirit and evidence of speaking in tongues.

Acts 2:4, 4:29–31, 8:15–25, 8:35–39, 9:1–19, 16:30–32, 18:8, 19:3–7